LEARNING TOGETHER

ADVICE AND INSTRUCTIONS ON COMPLETING THESE TESTS

1. There are 75 questions in each test. Make sure you have not missed a page.

2. Start at question 1 and work your way to question 75.

3. If you are unable to complete a question leave it and go to the next one.

4. Do not think about the question you have just left as this wastes time.

5. If you change an answer make sure the change is clear.

6. Each test should take approximately 40 minutes.

7. When you have finished each test mark it with an adult.

8. An adult or parent may be able to explain any questions you do not understand.

$$\frac{3}{6} \div \frac{4}{8} =$$

$$\frac{3}{6} \times \frac{8}{4} = \frac{24}{24}$$

TEST 06

SCORE _____

Which two are exactly the same? Circle two letters each time.

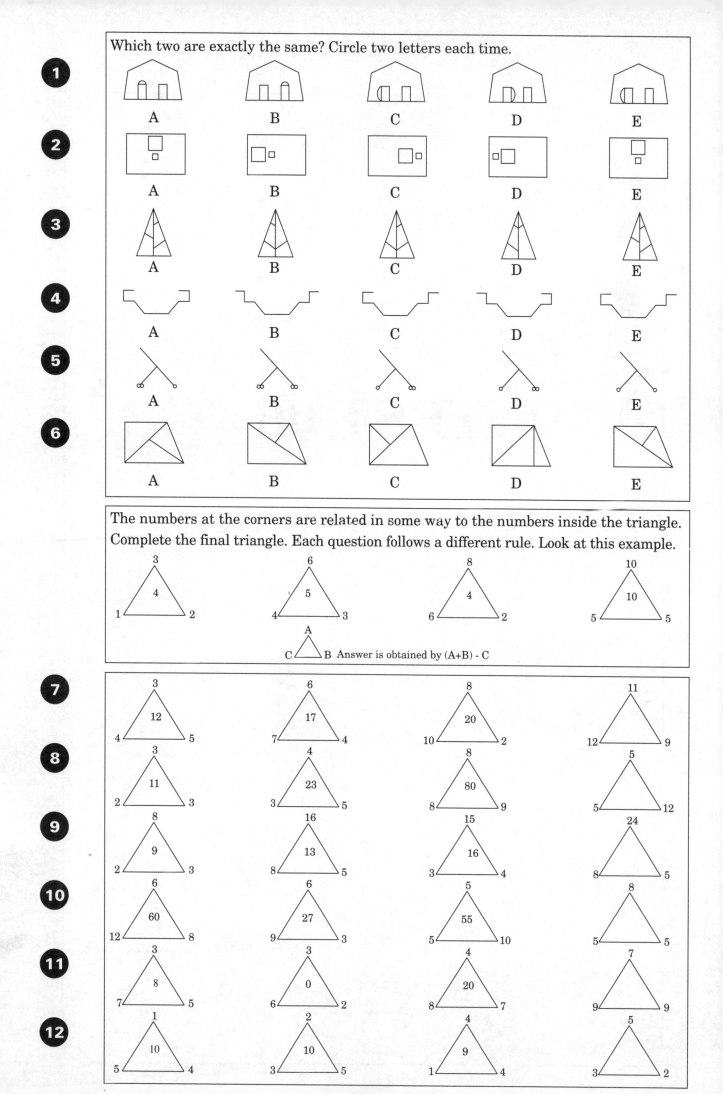

1 A B C D E

2 A B C D E

3 A B C D E

4 A B C D E

5 A B C D E

6 A B C D E

The numbers at the corners are related in some way to the numbers inside the triangle. Complete the final triangle. Each question follows a different rule. Look at this example.

Answer is obtained by (A+B) - C

In these questions the two shapes are either added together or subtracted from each other. The shapes do not turn. Circle one answer. Look at this example:

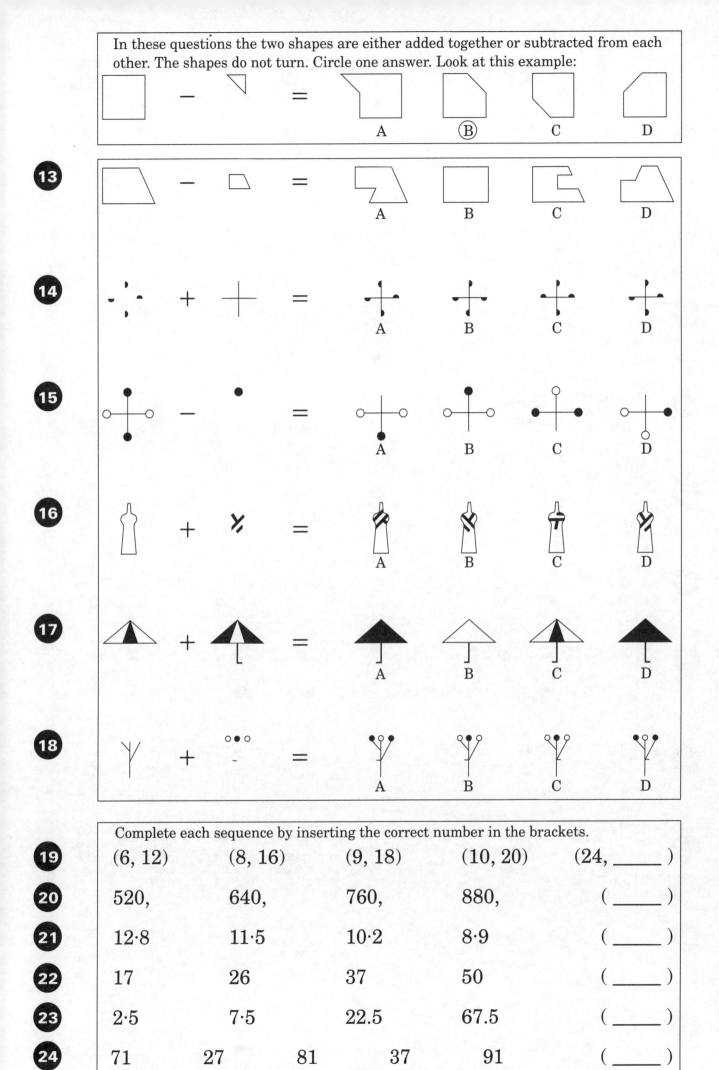

13

14

15

16

17

18

Complete each sequence by inserting the correct number in the brackets.

19 (6, 12) (8, 16) (9, 18) (10, 20) (24, _____)

20 520, 640, 760, 880, (_____)

21 12·8 11·5 10·2 8·9 (_____)

22 17 26 37 50 (_____)

23 2·5 7·5 22.5 67.5 (_____)

24 71 27 81 37 91 (_____)

Analogies. Circle one letter each time. Look at this example.

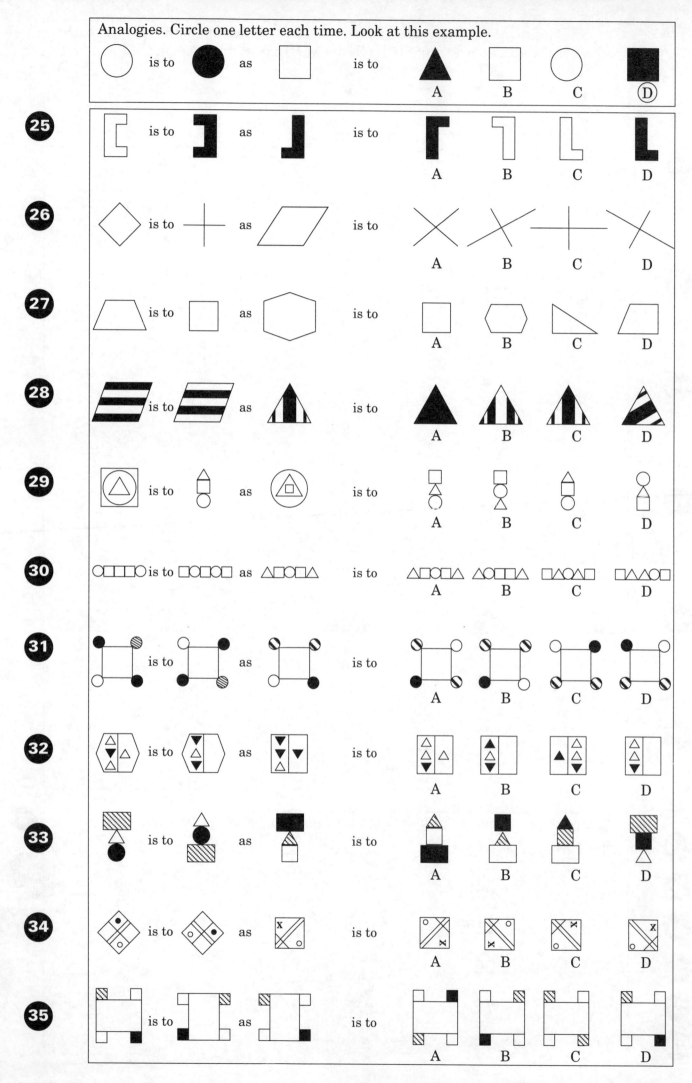

TEST 06 PAGE 3

The numbers in the right hand column are connected to those in the left hand column. Complete the brackets. Each question follows a different rule.

36

6 ⟶ 18

8 ⟶ 24

10 ⟶ 30

15 ⟶ (___)

37

26 ⟶ 13

34 ⟶ 17

56 ⟶ 28

82 ⟶ (___)

38

4 ⟶ 1

36 ⟶ 9

44 ⟶ 11

120 ⟶ (___)

Which shape is the same but facing the opposite direction? Look at this example:

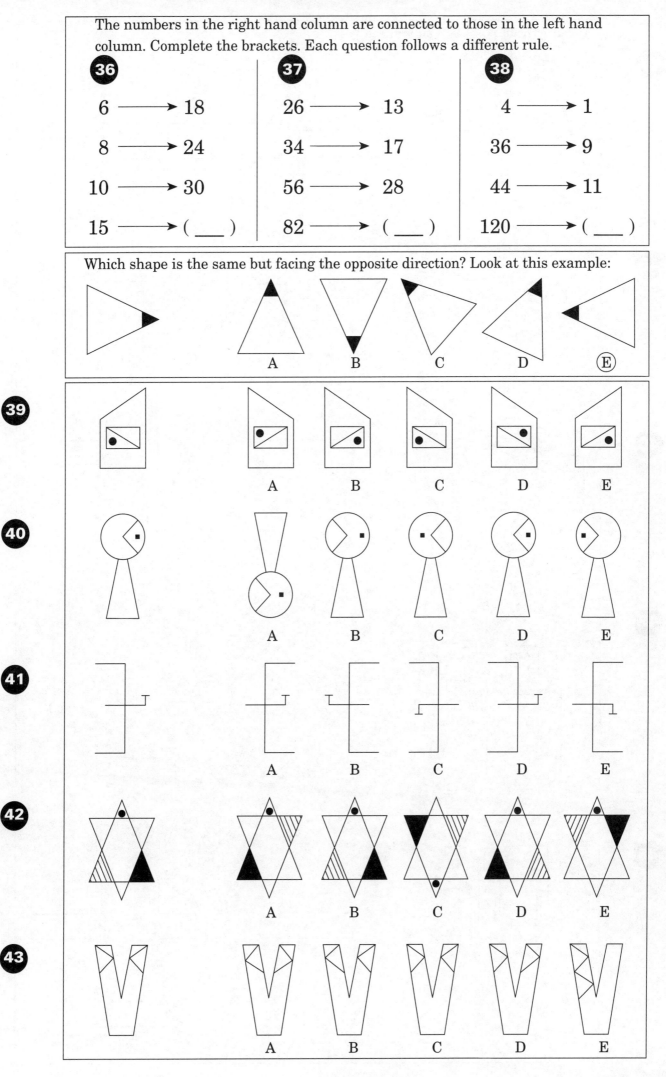

A B C D (E)

39

A B C D E

40

A B C D E

41

A B C D E

42

A B C D E

43

A B C D E

Looking from point 'X' you will see

44

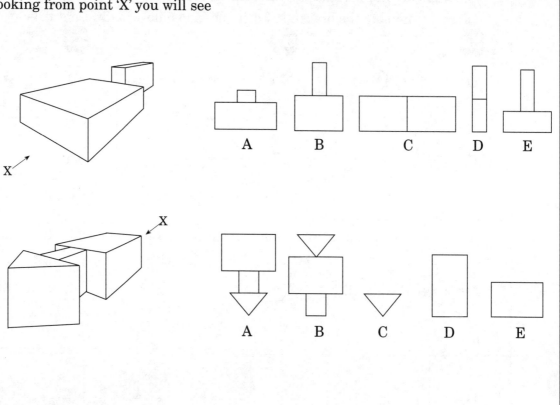

A   B   C   D   E

45

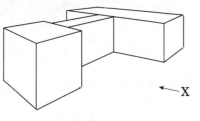

A   B   C   D   E

46

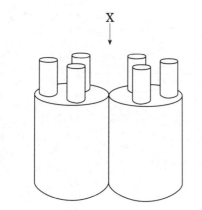

A   B   C

D   E

47

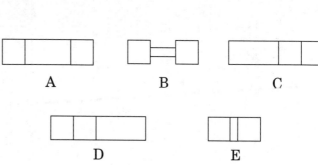

A   B   C

D   E

48

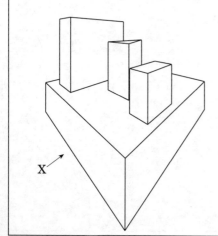

A   B   C

D   E

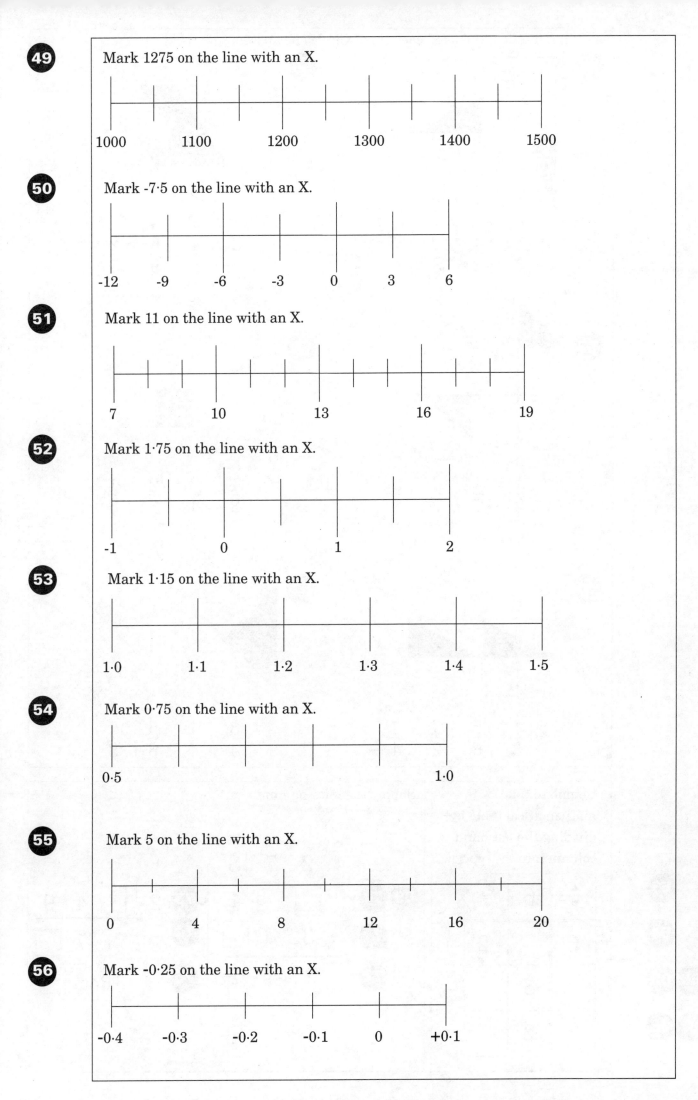

49 Mark 1275 on the line with an X.

1000 1100 1200 1300 1400 1500

50 Mark -7·5 on the line with an X.

-12 -9 -6 -3 0 3 6

51 Mark 11 on the line with an X.

7 10 13 16 19

52 Mark 1·75 on the line with an X.

-1 0 1 2

53 Mark 1·15 on the line with an X.

1·0 1·1 1·2 1·3 1·4 1·5

54 Mark 0·75 on the line with an X.

0·5 1·0

55 Mark 5 on the line with an X.

0 4 8 12 16 20

56 Mark -0·25 on the line with an X.

-0·4 -0·3 -0·2 -0·1 0 +0·1

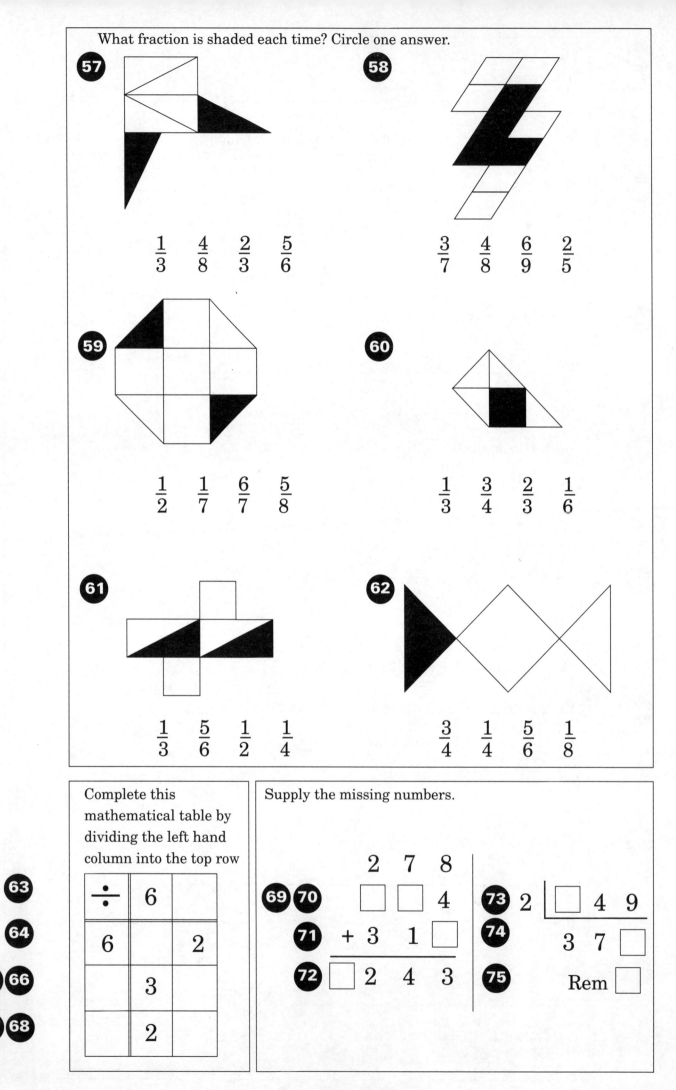

What fraction is shaded each time? Circle one answer.

57 $\frac{1}{3}$ $\frac{4}{8}$ $\frac{2}{3}$ $\frac{5}{6}$

58 $\frac{3}{7}$ $\frac{4}{8}$ $\frac{6}{9}$ $\frac{2}{5}$

59 $\frac{1}{2}$ $\frac{1}{7}$ $\frac{6}{7}$ $\frac{5}{8}$

60 $\frac{1}{3}$ $\frac{3}{4}$ $\frac{2}{3}$ $\frac{1}{6}$

61 $\frac{1}{3}$ $\frac{5}{6}$ $\frac{1}{2}$ $\frac{1}{4}$

62 $\frac{3}{4}$ $\frac{1}{4}$ $\frac{5}{6}$ $\frac{1}{8}$

Complete this mathematical table by dividing the left hand column into the top row

63
64
65 66
67 68

÷	6	
6		2
	3	
	2	

Supply the missing numbers.

69 70
71
72

```
    2 7 8
  □ □ 4
+ 3 1 □
─────────
□ 2 4 3
```

73
74
75

```
2 ) □ 4 9
    3 7 □
  Rem □
```

TEST 07

SCORE _____

Which two are exactly the same? Circle two letters each time.

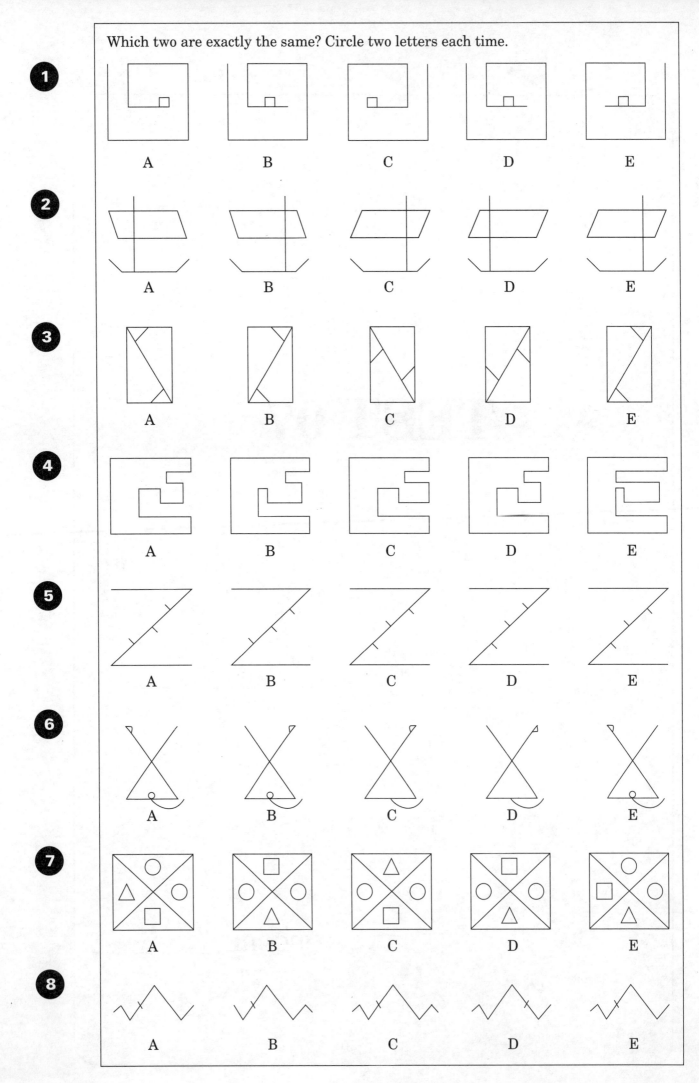

Which shape is the same but facing the opposite direction?
Circle one letter each time. Look at this example.

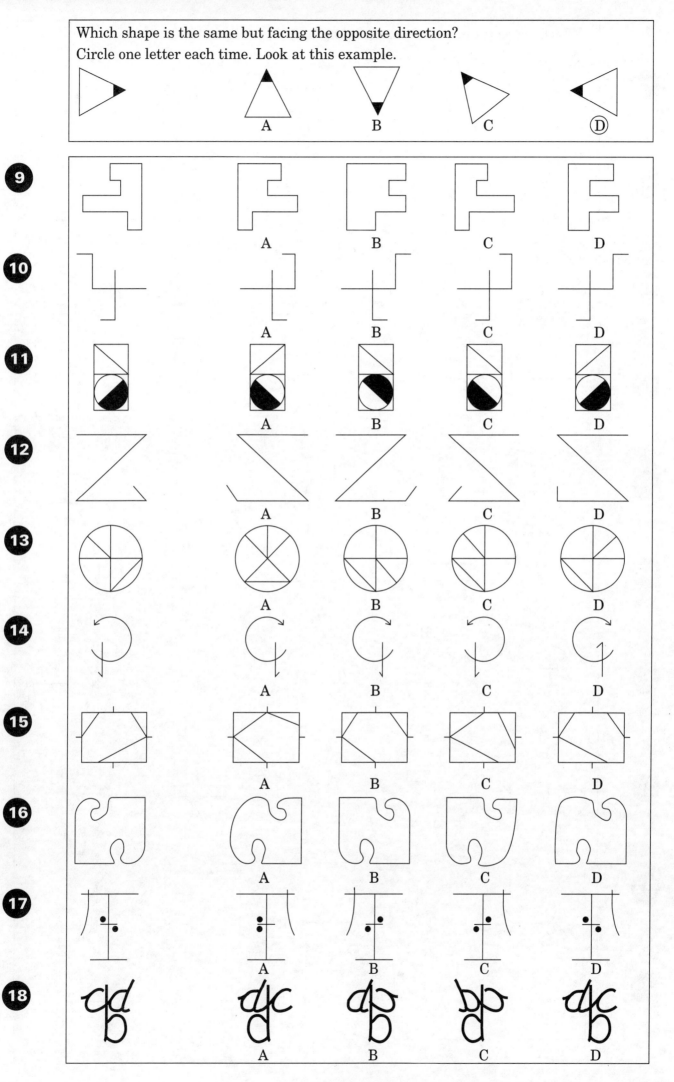

Which shape is different from the other four? Circle one letter each time.

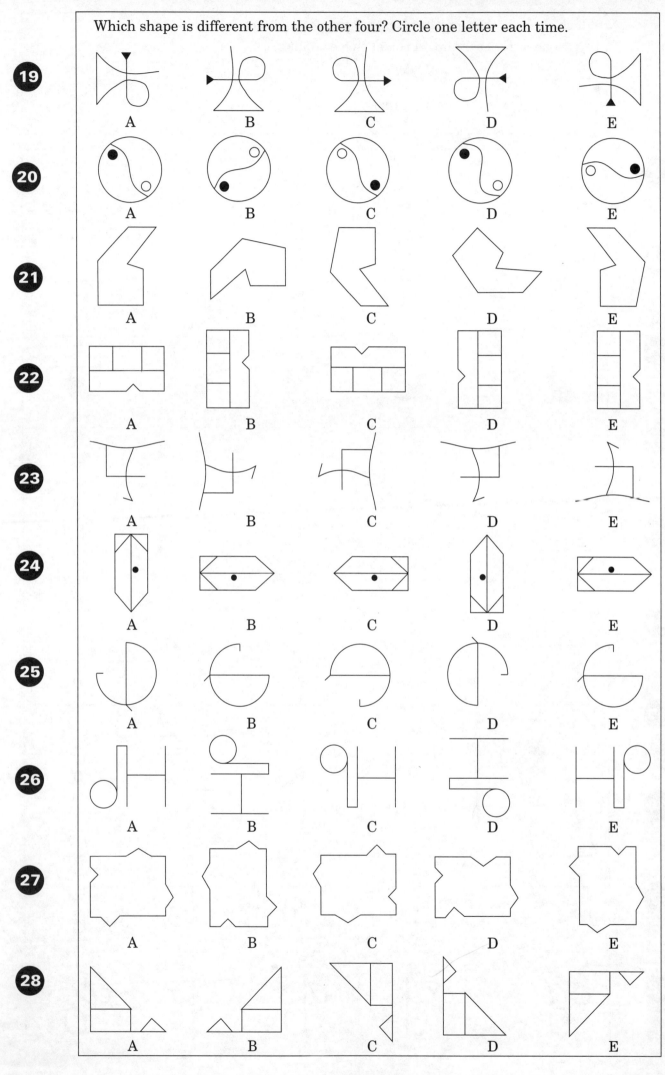

19   A   B   C   D   E

20   A   B   C   D   E

21   A   B   C   D   E

22   A   B   C   D   E

23   A   B   C   D   E

24   A   B   C   D   E

25   A   B   C   D   E

26   A   B   C   D   E

27   A   B   C   D   E

28   A   B   C   D   E

Which is the odd one out in this group of shapes? Circle one letter each time.
Look at this example.

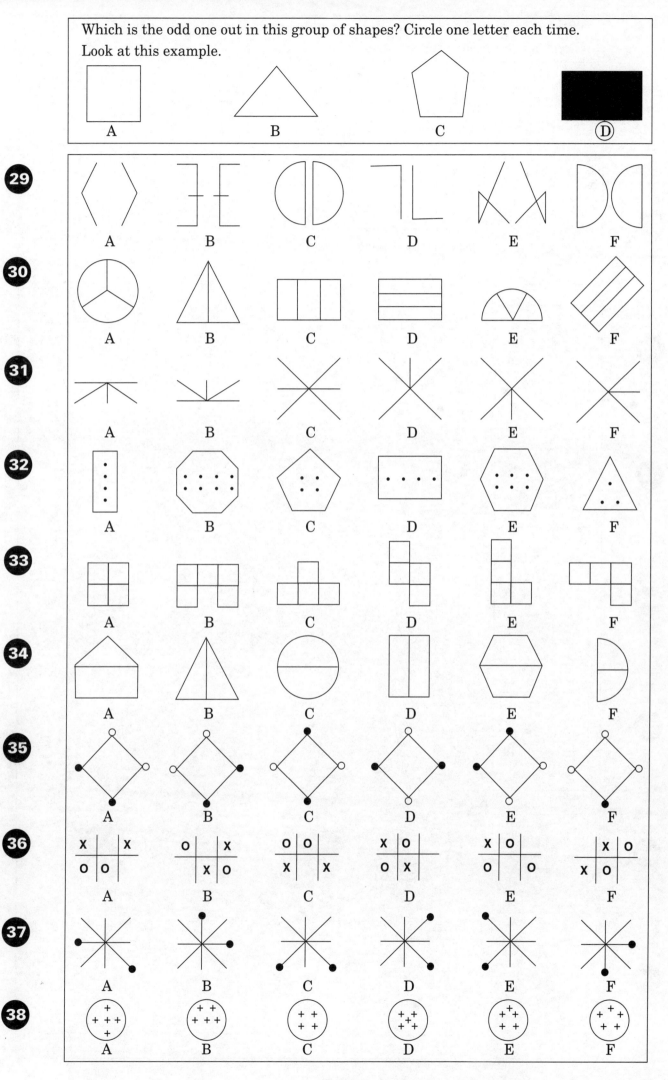

Without turning the pieces over choose which piece completes the white jig-saw.
Circle one letter each time.

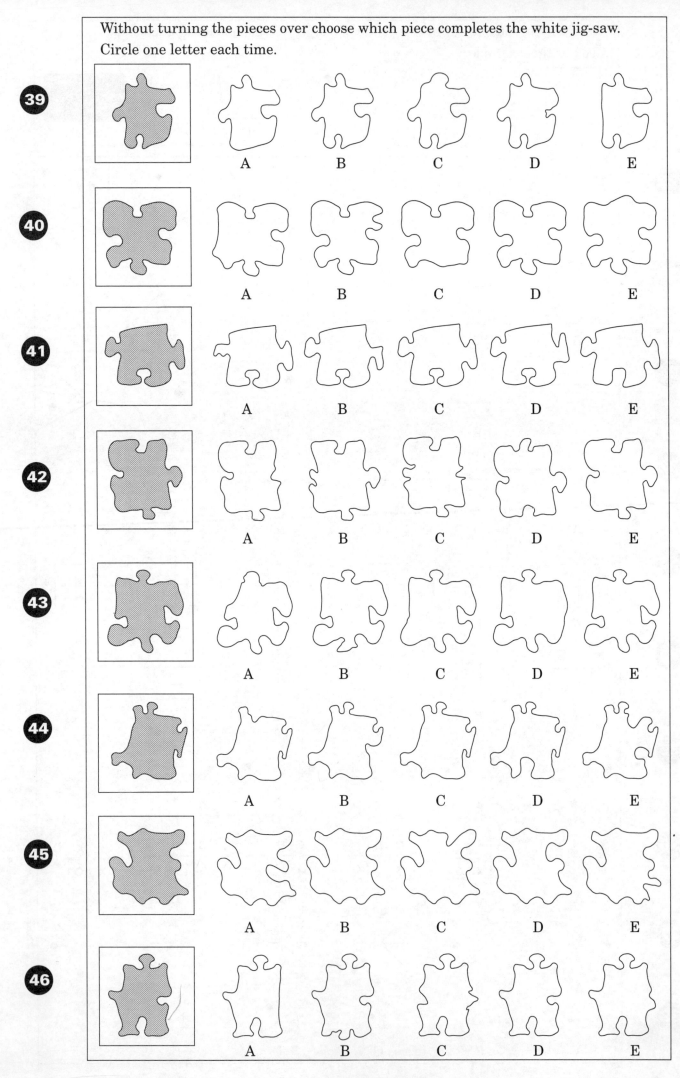

39   A   B   C   D   E

40   A   B   C   D   E

41   A   B   C   D   E

42   A   B   C   D   E

43   A   B   C   D   E

44   A   B   C   D   E

45   A   B   C   D   E

46   A   B   C   D   E

What comes next in this series? Circle one letter each time. Look at this example.

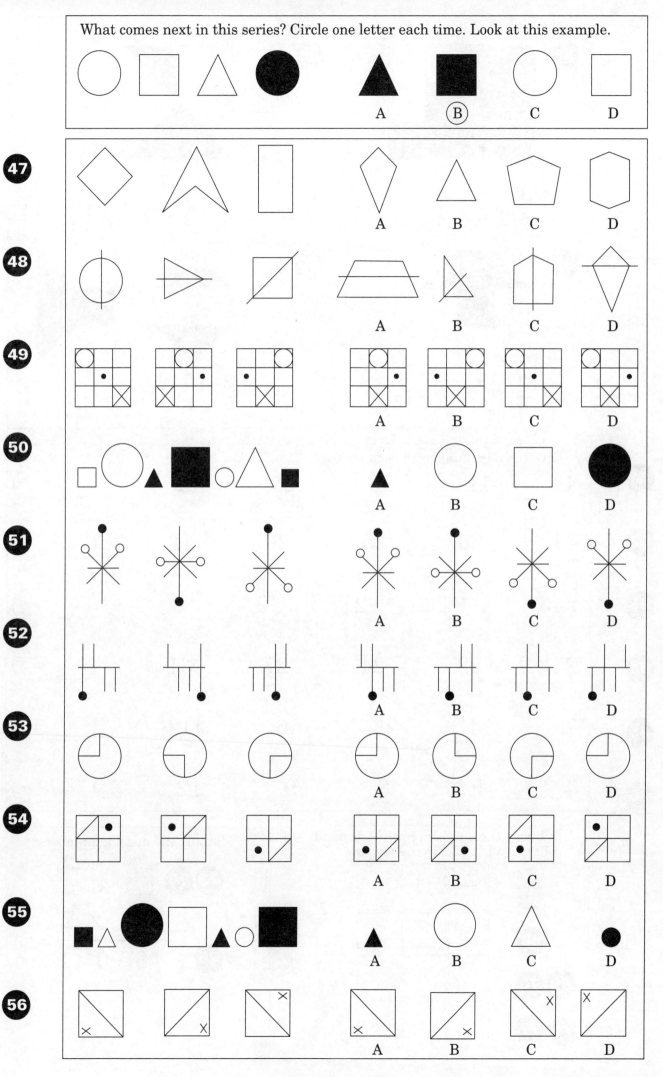

A   B   C   D

47

48

49

50

51

52

53

54

55

56

What fraction is shaded each time? Circle one answer.

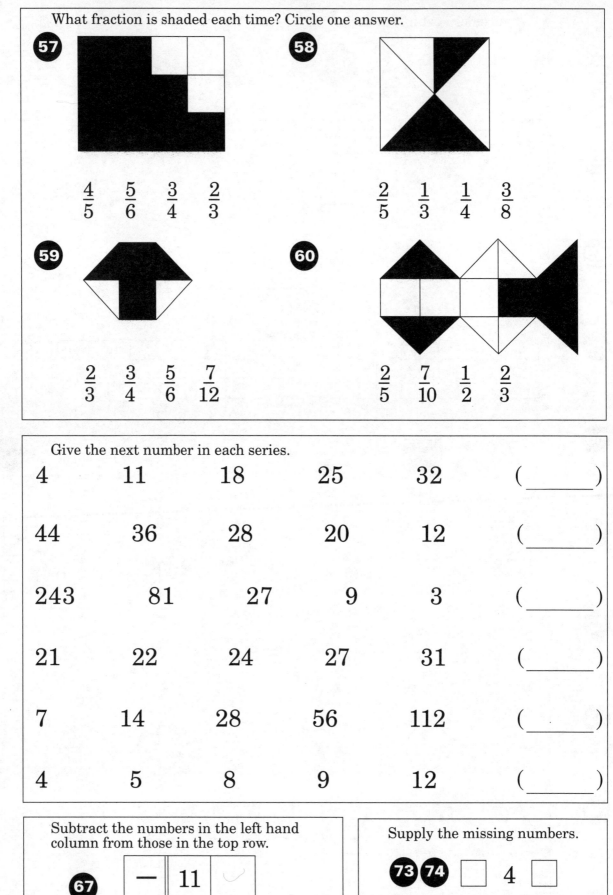

57 $\dfrac{4}{5}$ $\dfrac{5}{6}$ $\dfrac{3}{4}$ $\dfrac{2}{3}$

58 $\dfrac{2}{5}$ $\dfrac{1}{3}$ $\dfrac{1}{4}$ $\dfrac{3}{8}$

59 $\dfrac{2}{3}$ $\dfrac{3}{4}$ $\dfrac{5}{6}$ $\dfrac{7}{12}$

60 $\dfrac{2}{5}$ $\dfrac{7}{10}$ $\dfrac{1}{2}$ $\dfrac{2}{3}$

Give the next number in each series.

61 4   11   18   25   32   (____)

62 44   36   28   20   12   (____)

63 243   81   27   9   3   (____)

64 21   22   24   27   31   (____)

65 7   14   28   56   112   (____)

66 4   5   8   9   12   (____)

Subtract the numbers in the left hand column from those in the top row.

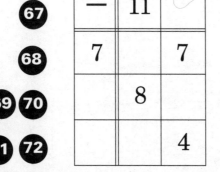

$-$	11	
67		
68 7		7
69 **70**	8	
71 **72**		4

Supply the missing numbers.

73 **74** ☐ 4 ☐

        x 7

75 ☐ 8 0 1

TEST 08

SCORE _____

Which is the odd one out in this group of shapes? Circle one letter each time.
Look at this example.

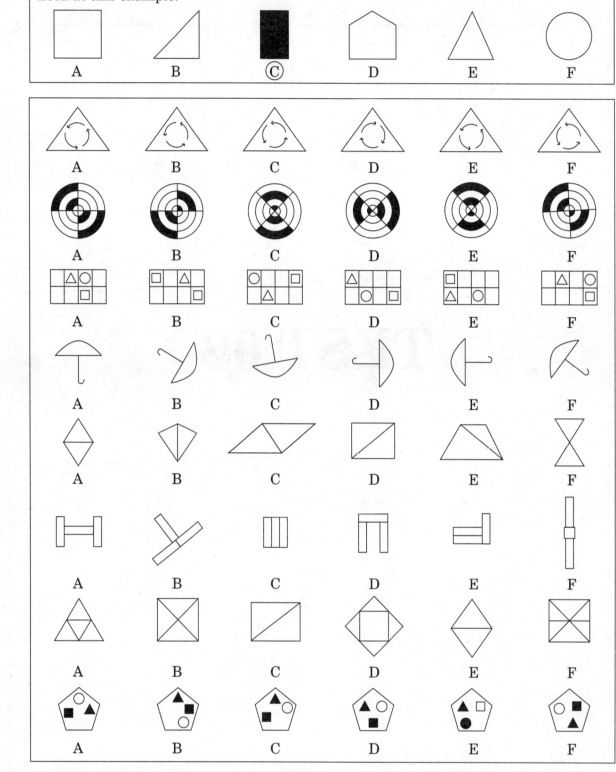

Complete the equation by putting the missing number in the bracket
given that 16 x 12 = 192.

9   17 x 12 = 192 + (____)

10   16 x 8 + (____) = 192

11   192 - (____) = 12 x 14

Look at the shape on the left. Which shadow matches the shape on the left exactly?
Circle one letter each time.

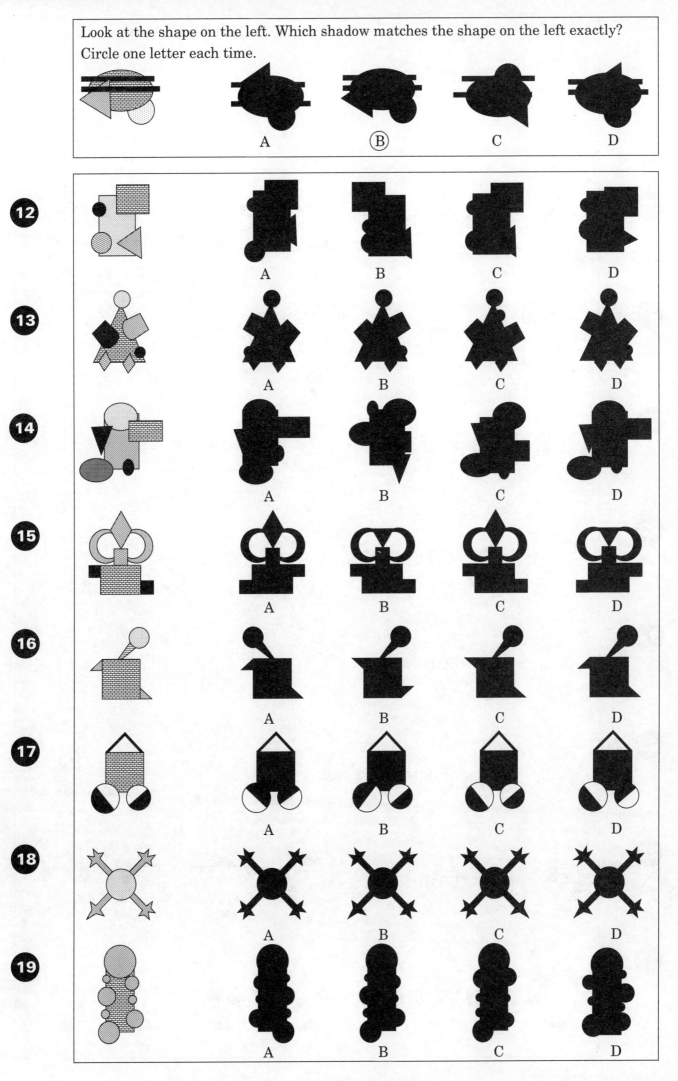

A   B   C   D

12   A   B   C   D

13   A   B   C   D

14   A   B   C   D

15   A   B   C   D

16   A   B   C   D

17   A   B   C   D

18   A   B   C   D

19   A   B   C   D

Folding and unfolding. Look at this example. Circle one letter each time.

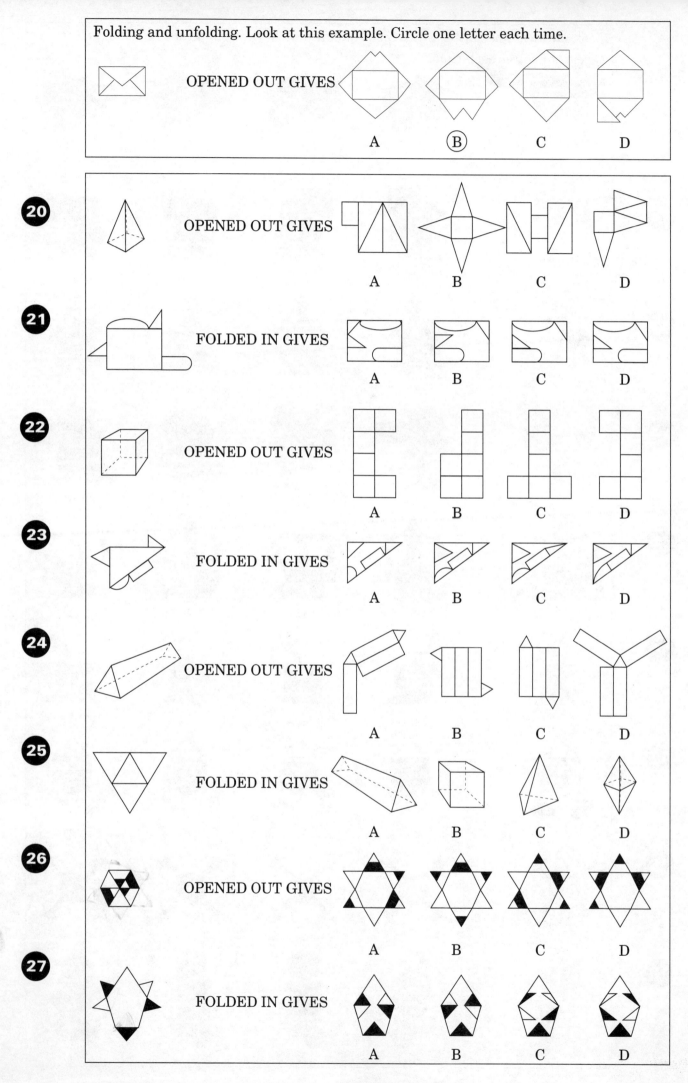

OPENED OUT GIVES

A B C D

20 OPENED OUT GIVES

A B C D

21 FOLDED IN GIVES

A B C D

22 OPENED OUT GIVES

A B C D

23 FOLDED IN GIVES

A B C D

24 OPENED OUT GIVES

A B C D

25 FOLDED IN GIVES

A B C D

26 OPENED OUT GIVES

A B C D

27 FOLDED IN GIVES

A B C D

Which two are exactly the same? Circle two letters each time.

28

A   B   C   D   E   F

29

A   B   C   D   E   F

30

A   B   C   D   E   F

31

A   B   C   D   E   F

32

A   B   C   D   E   F

33

A   B   C   D   E   F

Give the next number in each series.

34   8,   16,   32,   64,   (   )

35   17,   34,   51,   68,   (   )

36   405,   135,   45,   15,   (   )

37   36,   45,   54,   63,   (   )

What comes next in each series? Circle one letter each time.
Look at this example.

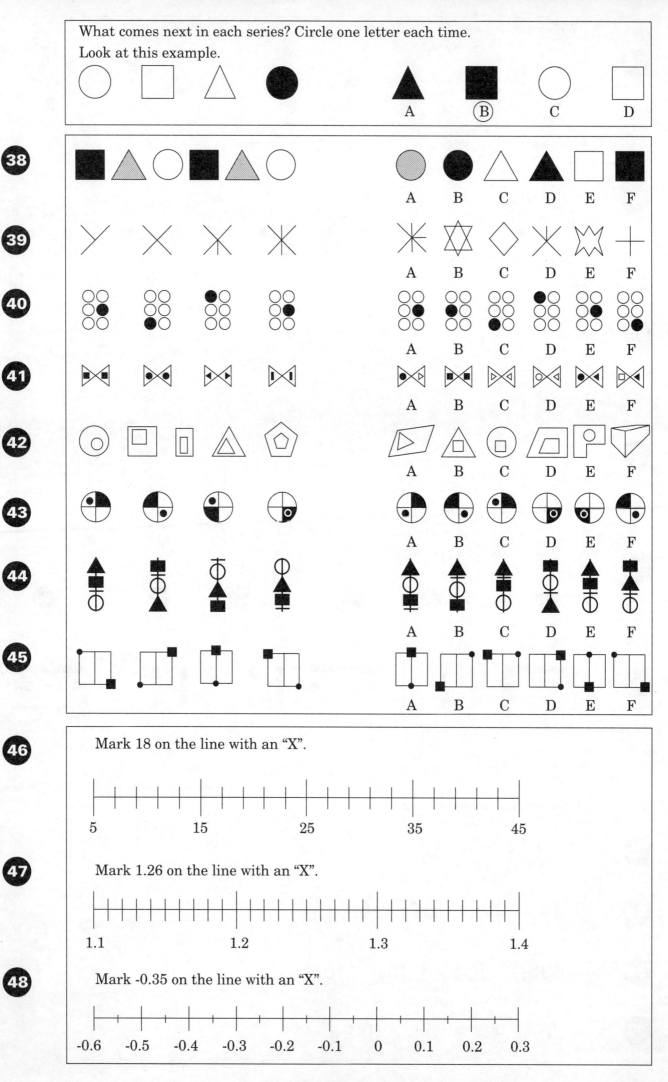

Looking from point X what will you see? Circle one letter each time.

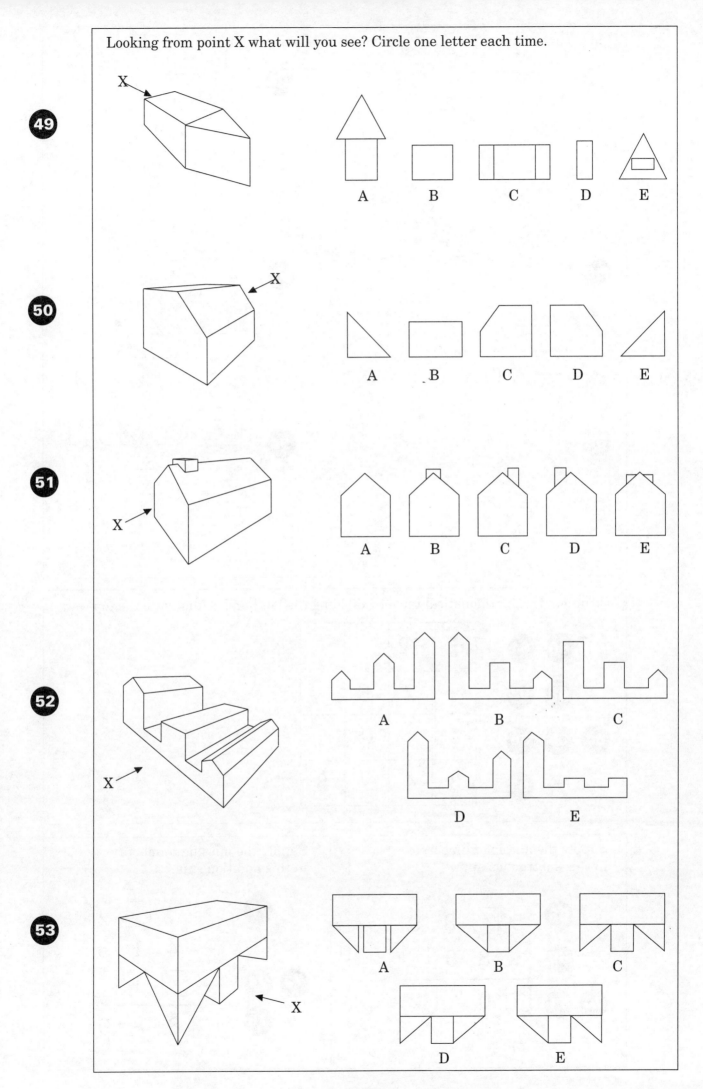

49

A B C D E

50

A B C D E

51

A B C D E

52

A B C

D E

53

A B C

D E

How many shapes like 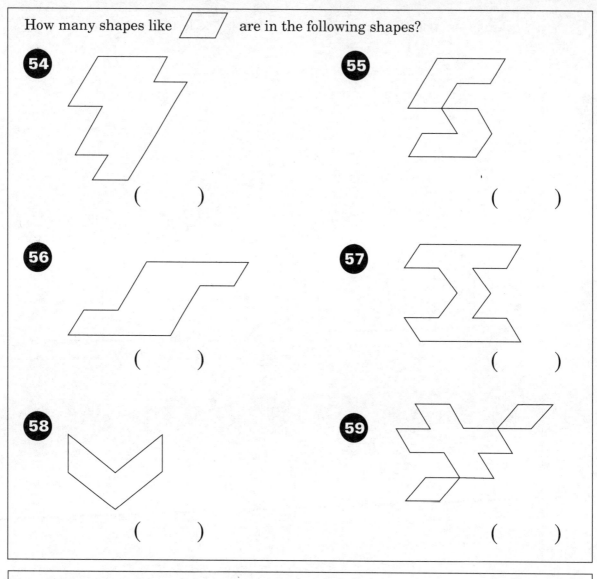 are in the following shapes?

54 ( )

55 ( )

56 ( )

57 ( )

58 ( )

59 ( )

Complete this mathematical table by dividing the left hand column into the top row.

60 **61**
62 **63**
64 **65** **66**
67

÷	12		
	2	6	
		18	
3	4		8

Supply the missing numbers in this subtraction sum.

68   5 ☐ 8 9
69 − 8 9 ☐
70 **71** ☐ 0 ☐ 2

Supply the missing numbers in this addition sum.

72   7 ☐ 2
             4 1 8
73 **74** + ☐ 1 ☐
75   ☐ 8 8 0

TEST 09

SCORE _____

Which shape is the same but facing the opposite direction?
Circle one letter each time. Look at this example.

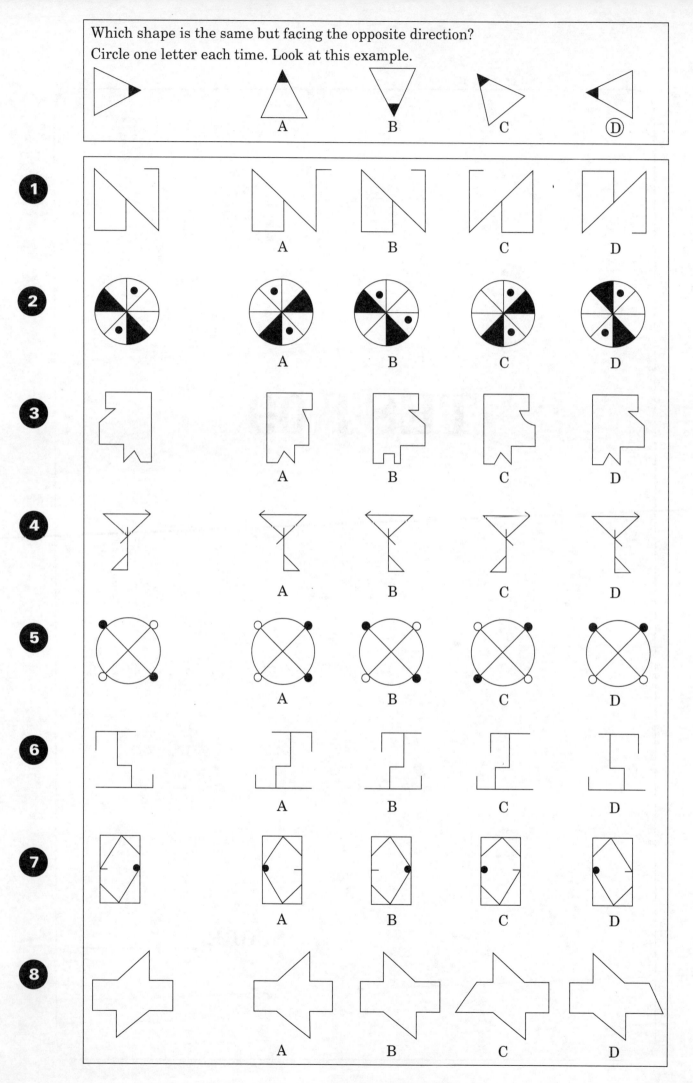

Which is the odd one out in this group of shapes? Circle one letter each time.
Look at this example.

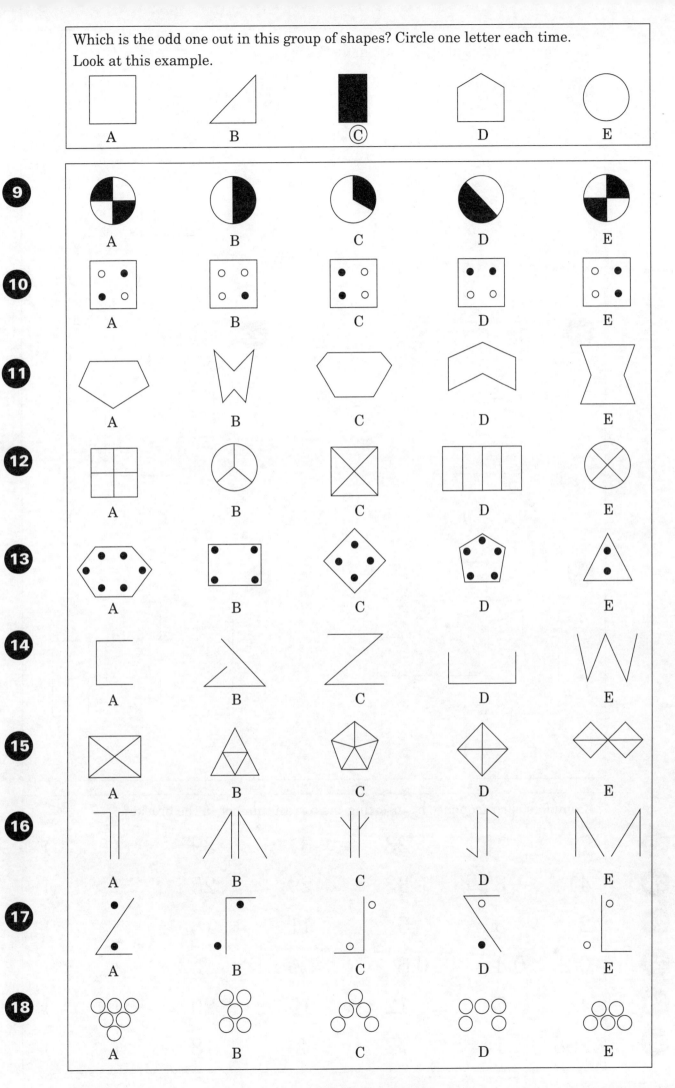

How many squares like ☐ are in the following shapes?

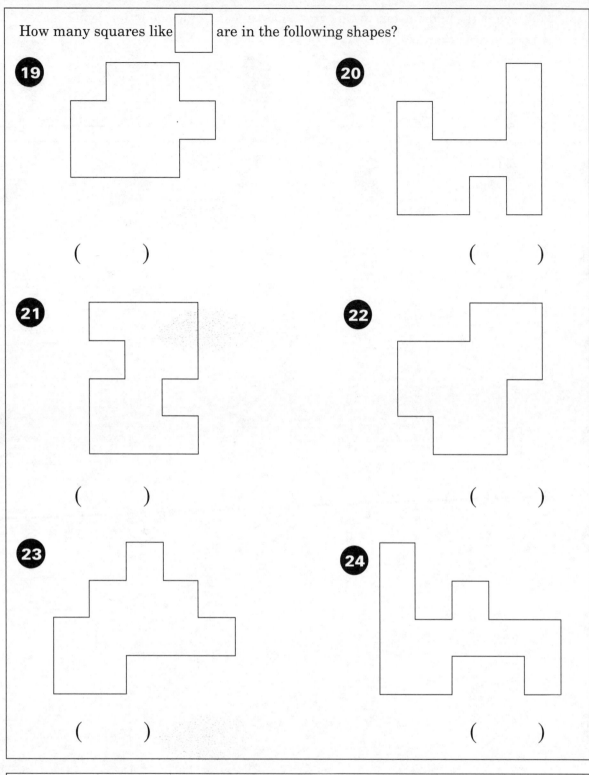

19 (　　)

20 (　　)

21 (　　)

22 (　　)

23 (　　)

24 (　　)

Complete each sequence by inserting the correct number in the brackets.

25	7	15	23	31	39	(　　)
26	41	37	33	29	25	(　　)
27	2	3	6	11	18	(　　)
28	0.2	0.4	0.8	1.6	3.2	(　　)
29	4	7	12	15	20	(　　)
30	288	144	72	36	18	(　　)

What comes next in each series? Circle one letter each time.
Look at this example.

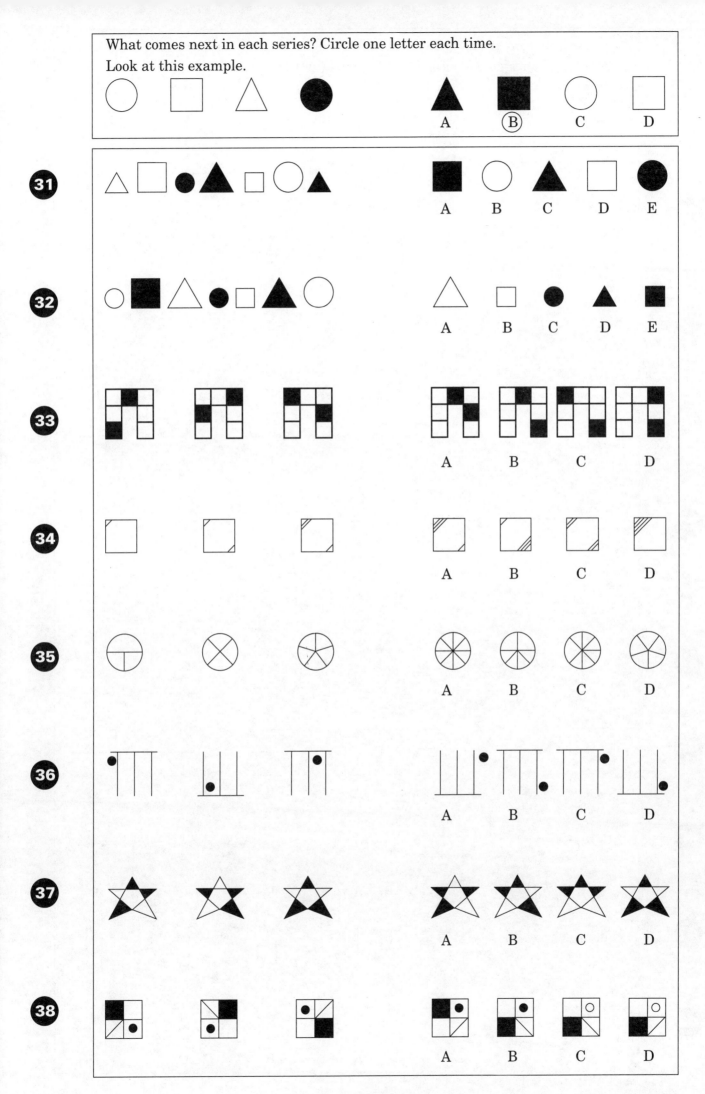

In these questions the two shapes are either added together or subtracted from each other. The shapes do not turn. Circle one answer. Look at this example.

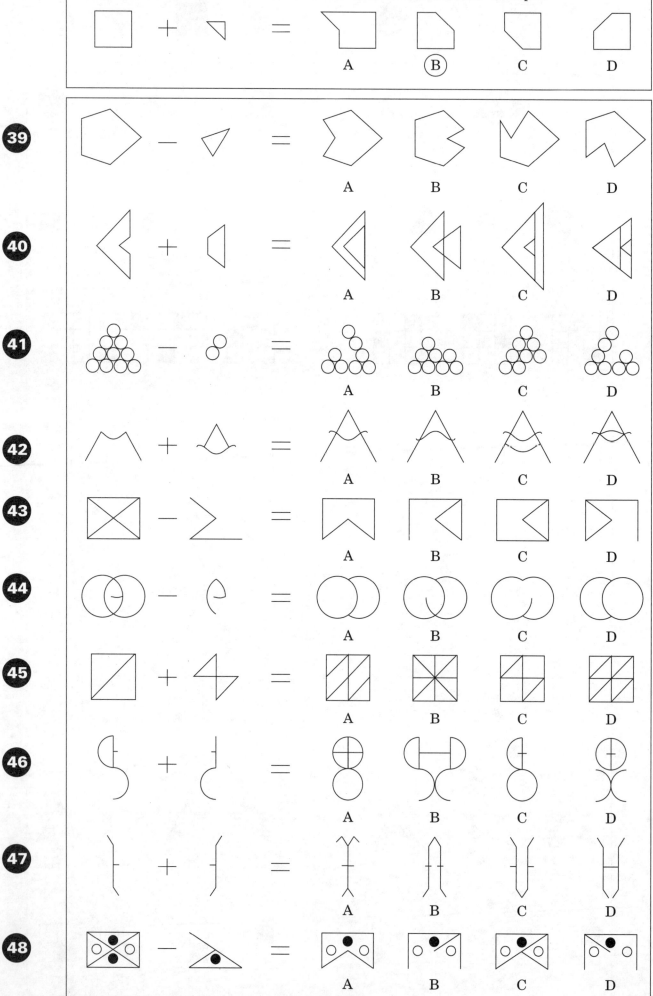

39

A   B   C   D

40

A   B   C   D

41

A   B   C   D

42

A   B   C   D

43

A   B   C   D

44

A   B   C   D

45

A   B   C   D

46

A   B   C   D

47

A   B   C   D

48

A   B   C   D

Which shape is different from the other four? Circle one letter each time.

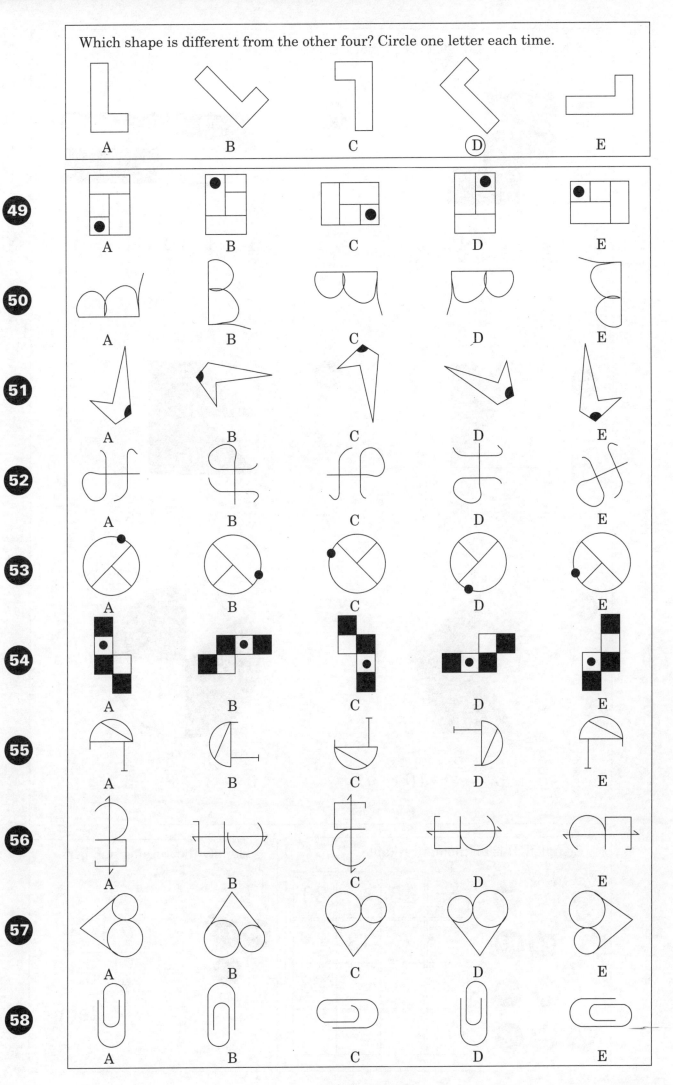

What fraction is shaded each time? Circle one answer.

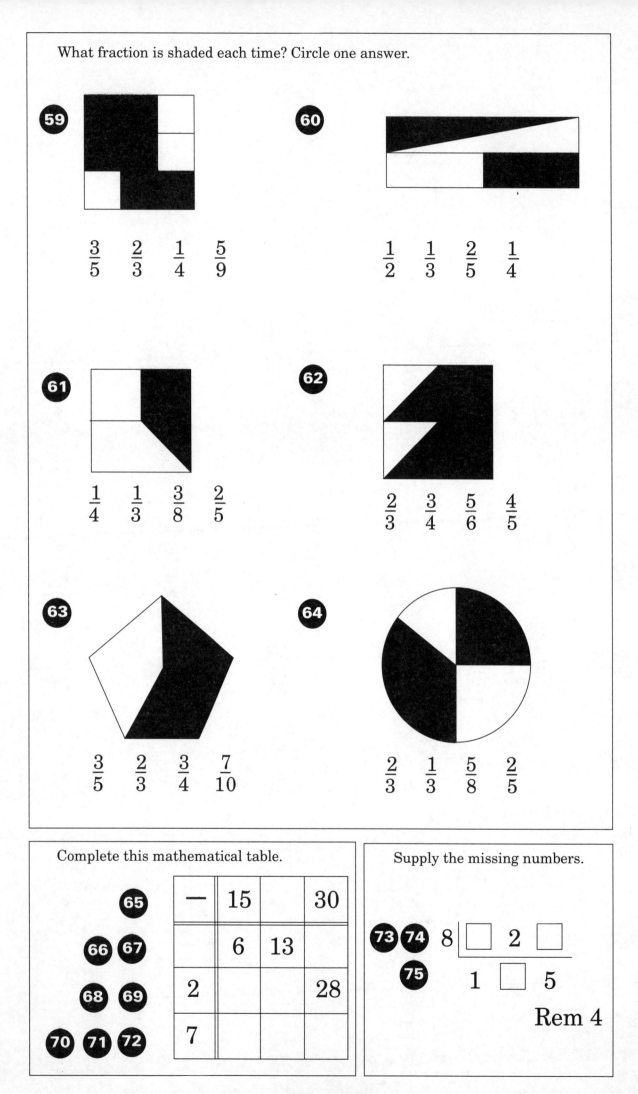

59

$\dfrac{3}{5}$ $\dfrac{2}{3}$ $\dfrac{1}{4}$ $\dfrac{5}{9}$

60

$\dfrac{1}{2}$ $\dfrac{1}{3}$ $\dfrac{2}{5}$ $\dfrac{1}{4}$

61

$\dfrac{1}{4}$ $\dfrac{1}{3}$ $\dfrac{3}{8}$ $\dfrac{2}{5}$

62

$\dfrac{2}{3}$ $\dfrac{3}{4}$ $\dfrac{5}{6}$ $\dfrac{4}{5}$

63

$\dfrac{3}{5}$ $\dfrac{2}{3}$ $\dfrac{3}{4}$ $\dfrac{7}{10}$

64

$\dfrac{2}{3}$ $\dfrac{1}{3}$ $\dfrac{5}{8}$ $\dfrac{2}{5}$

Complete this mathematical table.

65

66 **67**

68 **69**

70 **71** **72**

—	15		30
	6	13	
2			28
7			

Supply the missing numbers.

73 **74**

75

$$8 \boxed{} \; 2 \; \boxed{}$$
$$1 \; \boxed{} \; 5$$

Rem 4

TEST 09 PAGE 7

TEST 10

SCORE _____

What comes next in this series? Circle one letter each time.
Look at this example.

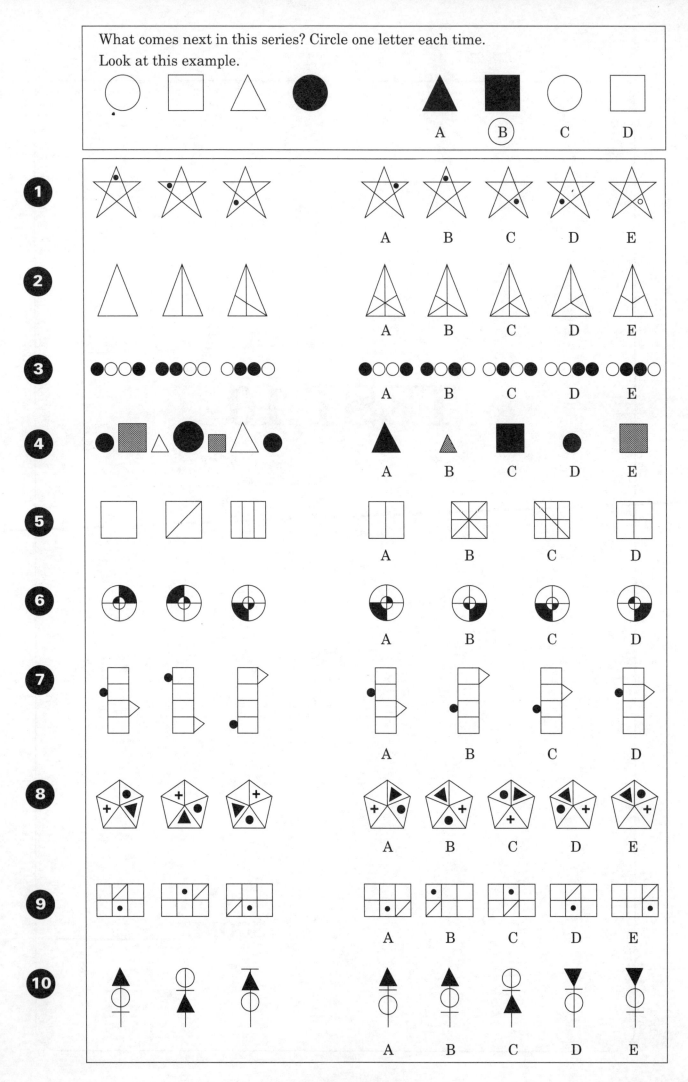

Analogies. Circle one letter each time. Look at this example:

○ is to ● as ☐ is to ▲(A) ☐(B) ○(C) ■(D)

A   B   C   (D)

11 ↓ is to ← as ⊙ is to ... A   B   C   D

12 is to as ▽ is to ... A   B   C   D

13 X is to as H is to ... A   B   C   D

14 is to as is to ... A   B   C   D

15 is to as is to ... A   B   C   D

16 is to ☐ as is to ... A   B   C   D

17 is to as is to ... A   B   C   D

18 is to as is to ... A   B   C   D

19 is to as is to ... A   B   C   D

20 is to as is to ... A   B   C   D

Without turning the pieces over choose which piece completes the white jig-saw pieces. Circle one letter each time.

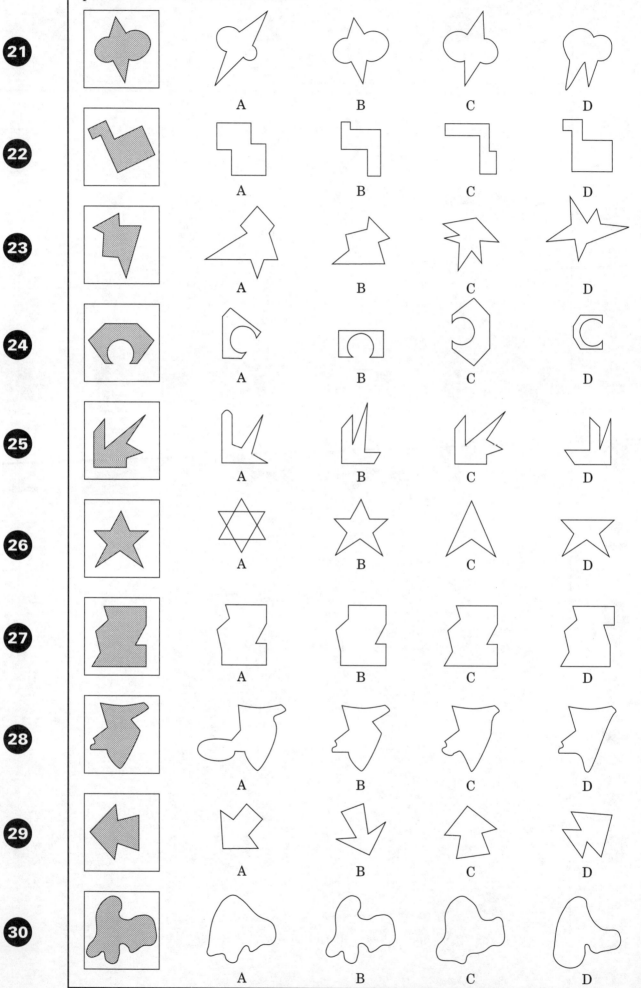

21
A   B   C   D

22
A   B   C   D

23
A   B   C   D

24
A   B   C   D

25
A   B   C   D

26
A   B   C   D

27
A   B   C   D

28
A   B   C   D

29
A   B   C   D

30
A   B   C   D

Which larger shape is the small shape hidden in? Look at this example:

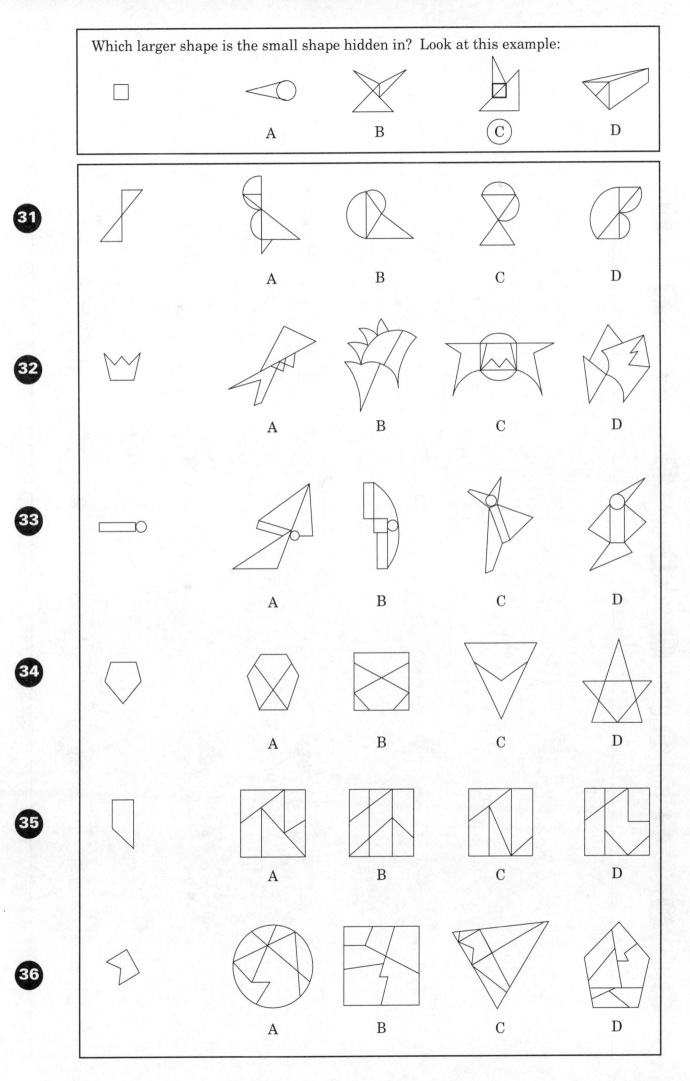

A B C D

31

32

33

34

35

36

A B C D

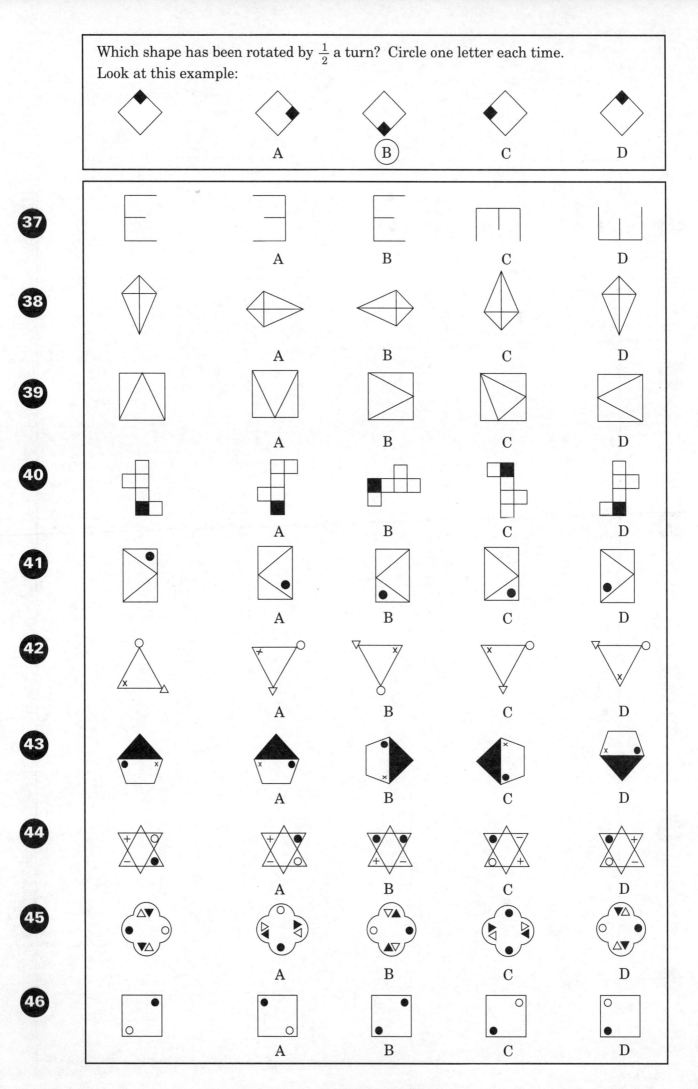

Which shape has been rotated by $\frac{1}{2}$ a turn? Circle one letter each time.
Look at this example:

A   B   C   D

37

38

39

40

41

42

43

44

45

46

Which shape does not have a horizontal or a verticle line of symmetry?
Circle one letter each time.

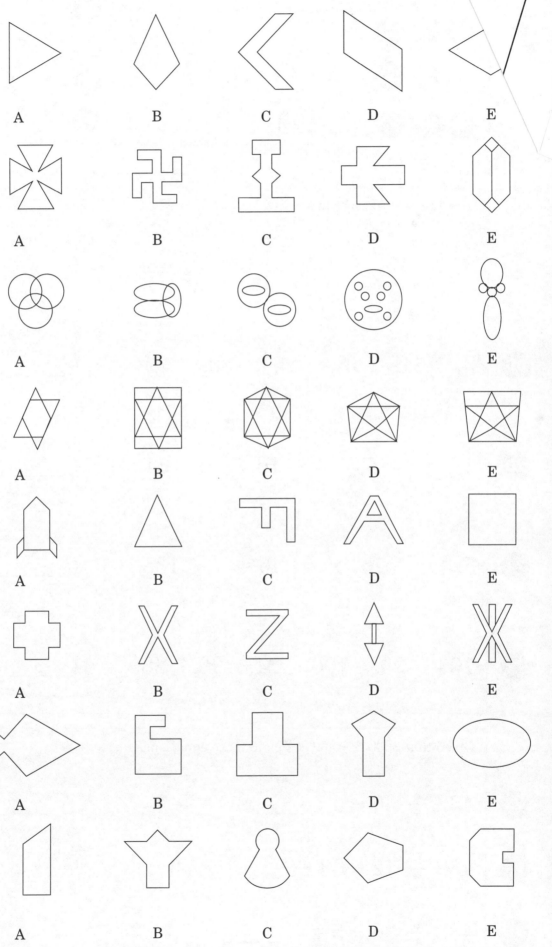

47 A B C D E

48 A B C D E

49 A B C D E

50 A B C D E

51 A B C D E

52 A B C D E

53 A B C D E

54 A B C D E

55

X	6		3
		40	
4		32	
	42		

56 **57** **58**

59 **60**

61 **62** **63**

Supply the missing numbers.

64 9 ☐ 5
65 ☐ 5 8
66 + 2 4 ☐
67 ☐ 8 7 6

Give the next number in each series.

68 8, 7 15, 9 24, 11 35, 13 48 15 (_63_)

69 2,   11,   16,   25,   30,   39   (_____)

70 1,   4,   16,   64   (_____)

71 5,   15,   45,   135   (_____)

72 104,   20,   100,   24,   96,   28   (_____)

Given that 36 X 12 = 432 complete these equations.

73 432 ÷ 36 = (_____)

74 432 ÷ 12 = 38 - (_____)

75 432 ÷ 36 = 5 + (_____)

1.	B and D
2.	C and E
3.	B and E
4.	A and D
5.	C and E
6.	A and E
7.	B and D
8.	A and E
9.	C
10.	B
11.	A
12.	C
13.	D
14.	A
15.	D
16.	B
17.	C
18.	C
19.	C
20.	D
21.	A
22.	E
23.	D
24.	B
25.	C
26.	C
27.	D
28.	A
29.	D
30.	B
31.	C
32.	C
33.	B
34.	A
35.	F
36.	E
37.	A
38.	C
39.	B
40.	D
41.	C
42.	E
43.	E
44.	C
45.	B
46.	D
47.	A
48.	C
49.	C
50.	D
51.	D
52.	C
53.	B
54.	B
55.	C
56.	D
57.	$\frac{3}{4}$
58.	$\frac{3}{8}$
59.	$\frac{3}{4}$
60.	$\frac{1}{2}$
61.	39
62.	4
63.	1
64.	36
65.	224
66.	13
67.	14
68.	4
69.	3
70.	11
71.	10
72.	1
73.	5
74.	3
75.	3

A child who has not previously attempted questions of this type may have difficulty with the first few tests. However, research shows that a child's ability to handle and understand these questions generally increases with practice.

1.	C and E
2.	A and E
3.	A and E
4.	C and E
5.	C and D
6.	B and E
7.	32 A + B + C
8.	65 (A x B) + C
9.	21 (A + B) - C
10.	45 (A x B) + C
11.	54 (A x B) - C
12.	10 A + B + C
13.	C
14.	D
15.	A
16.	D
17.	D
18.	B
19.	48
20.	1000
21.	7.6
22.	65
23.	202.5
24.	47
25.	C
26.	B
27.	B
28.	B
29.	B
30.	C
31.	C
32.	D
33.	A
34.	C
35.	B
36.	45 (3 x)
37.	41 ($\frac{1}{2}$ x)
38.	30 (x ÷ 4)
39.	B
40.	E
41.	B
42.	D
43.	C
44.	A
45.	E
46.	A
47.	C
48.	D
49.	[number line: 1200 — 1300]
50.	[number line: -9 — -6]
51.	[number line: 10 — 13]
52.	[number line: 1 — 2]
53.	[number line: 1.1 — 2.2]
54.	[number line: 0.5 — 1.1]
55.	[number line: 4 — 8]
56.	[number line: -0.3 — -0.2]
57.	$\frac{1}{3}$
58.	$\frac{2}{5}$
59.	$\frac{1}{7}$
60.	$\frac{1}{3}$
61.	$\frac{1}{3}$
62.	$\frac{1}{4}$
63.	12
64.	1
65.	2
66.	6
67.	3
68.	4
69.	6
70.	5
71.	1
72.	1
73.	7
74.	3
75.	1

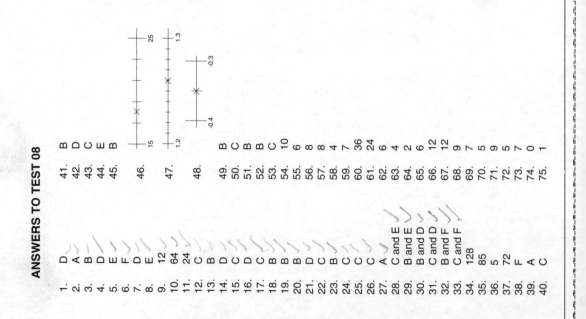

ANSWERS TO TEST 08

1.	D	41.	B
2.	A	42.	D
3.	B	43.	C
4.	D	44.	E
5.	E	45.	B
6.	F	46.	
7.	D	47.	
8.	E	48.	
9.	12	49.	B
10.	64	50.	C
11.	24	51.	B
12.	C	52.	B
13.	B	53.	C
14.	D	54.	10
15.	C	55.	6
16.	D	56.	8
17.	C	57.	8
18.	B	58.	4
19.	B	59.	7
20.	B	60.	36
21.	D	61.	24
22.	B	62.	6
23.	B	63.	4
24.	C	64.	2
25.	C	65.	6
26.	C	66.	12
27.	A	67.	12
28.	C and E	68.	9
29.	B and E	69.	7
30.	B and D	70.	5
31.	C and D	71.	9
32.	B and F	72.	5
33.	C and F	73.	9
34.	128	74.	0
35.	85	75.	1
36.	5		
37.	72		
38.	F		
39.	A		
40.	C		

ANSWERS TO TEST 09

1.	C	41.	D
2.	A	42.	A
3.	D	43.	B
4.	B	44.	C
5.	C	45.	D
6.	A	46.	C
7.	D	47.	D
8.	B	48.	B
9.	C	49.	B
10.	B	50.	C
11.	A	51.	A
12.	B	52.	D
13.	E	53.	E
14.	E	54.	A
15.	C	55.	B
16.	D	56.	C
17.	D	57.	C
18.	A	58.	C
19.	9	59.	$\frac{2}{3}$
20.	10	60.	$\frac{1}{2}$
21.	10	61.	$\frac{3}{8}$
22.	11	62.	$\frac{3}{4}$
23.	11	63.	$\frac{3}{5}$
24.	11	64.	$\frac{5}{8}$
25.	47	65.	22
26.	21	66.	9
27.	27	67.	21
28.	6.4	68.	13
29.	23	69.	20
30.	9	70.	8
31.	A	71.	15
32.	E	72.	23
33.	B	73.	9
34.	C	74.	4
35.	B	75.	1
36.	D		
37.	A		
38.	B		
39.	C		
40.	B		

ANSWERS TO TEST 10

1.	C	41.	B
2.	A	42.	B
3.	D	43.	D
4.	E	44.	C
5.	D	45.	B
6.	B	46.	C
7.	C	47.	D
8.	D	48.	B
9.	C	49.	C
10.	B	50.	A
11.	A	51.	C
12.	C	52.	C
13.	B	53.	B
14.	B	54.	A
15.	D	55.	8
16.	A	56.	5
17.	B	57.	30
18.	D	58.	15
19.	D	59.	24
20.	C	60.	12
21.	B	61.	7
22.	D	62.	56
23.	B	63.	21
24.	C	64.	7
25.	C	65.	6
26.	B	66.	3
27.	C	67.	1
28.	B	68.	63
29.	B	69.	44
30.	B	70.	256
31.	D	71.	405
32.	C	72.	92
33.	C	73.	12
34.	D	74.	2
35.	B	75.	7
36.	C		
37.	A		
38.	B		
39.	A		
40.	C		